LIBRARIES NI
WITHDRAWN

HOW TO BE A HERO

D0657261

With most books, you read from the beginning
to the end and then stop. You can then read it
backwards if you like, but that would be silly.

But in this book, you're the hero. That's why
it's called *I Hero*, see?

You read a bit, then you make a choice that
takes you to a different part of the book. You
might jump from Section 3 to Section 47 or
Section 28. Crazy, huh?

If you make a good choice, *GREAT!*

BUUUUUUT...

If you make the wrong choice, **ALL KINDS
OF BAD STUFF WILL HAPPEN.**

Hah-ha! Loser! You'll have to start again.

But that won't happen to you, will it?
Because you're not a zero — *YOU'RE A HERO!*

This is you! You are **ROBIN HAMSTER**, the leader of a band of outlaws. You live in the Greenwood. You fight for good and justice for all. You are a **GOODY**!

HURRAH!

These are some of your merry menagerie.

MAID MOUSIE   SMALL JOHN

MAID INCHINA   BILL SCARLETT

FRIAR CLUCK

Of course, all goodies have enemies, who are
BAD!

These are the **BADDIES**. They are **NOT**
a nice bunch...

BOOOOO!

GUY OF
GRIZZLYBUM

THE SHERIFF OF
SNOTTINGHAM
(he sneezes a lot)

PRINCESS JOAN

You have sworn to fight to protect the weak and helpless. You steal from the rich and give to the poor (and keep a little for yourself!).

You have heard that the sheriff's tax collector is heading through the forest on his way to Snottingham with a **LOT** of money! It's time for an **AMBUSH!**

Go to 1.

1

You are hiding in the branches of a great oak tree waiting for the **TAX COLLECTOR**. The other outlaws are hidden behind the trees and bushes of the forest.

You see the collector coming down the track. His wagon is pulled by two horses. You have several ways to spring the **ambush**.

If you wish to chop down a tree to block the path, go to 26.

If you wish to swing on a rope and land on the wagon, go to 18.

If you wish to leap down from the tree and demand that he stop, go to 43.

2

You wait until the guards have gone.

"Let's get out of this city," you say to Maid Mousie.

"And leave the gang here?" she says. "Are you a man or a mouse?"

"Actually, I'm a hamster..."

"I think you're a **CHICKEN**!"

She storms off, leaving you alone in the poo.

What sort of a leader are you? Hamster up and go back to 1.

3

At that moment a lookout in the trees calls out.

"INCOMING!"

The tax collector laughs. "The sheriff's men were following me! You've fallen into the trap!"

You look up to see dozens of mounted soldiers heading through the trees towards the camp.

If you want to fight the enemy, go to 31.

If you want to get away NOW, go to 45.

4

Taking your bow, you push your way through the queuing archers.

"Oi," says a wolf archer. "Stop pushing in. Get in line..."

If you wish to ignore him, go to 33.
If you wish to take your place in the queue, go to 17.

5

You give the order. "Fellow outlaws attack the..."

OOOF!

You get no further as the horses run you down. And just for good measure, the wagon wheels roll over the top of you...

You must be wheely, wheely sore!
Go back to 1.

6

You dive at the sheriff and send him hurtling into the pie. The four and twenty blackbirds fly around his head, tickling the sheriff with their feathers.

"STOP... STOP IT...

AT...ISHOOO!"

You look at the green mess on the floor.

"So, that's why you're the Sheriff of Snottingham!"

Go to 50.

7

"No, I will go on my own!" you say. "I am the leader and what I say goes!"

The outlaws shake their heads. "Well in that case, we're going," says Maid Mousie. "Not to Snottingham, but away from you and the Greenwood. Cheerio."

Despite your protests the outlaws head off, leaving you on your own.

That wasn't very clever, was it?
Go back to 1.

8

You shake your fist. "Let's see what you've got..."

The soldiers close in on you, rolling up their sleeves.

WHAM!
CRUNCH!

Actually, they've got a lot!
Go back to 1.

9

You make your way to the entrance. You run and with a great jump, leap up and grab hold of the wooden drawbridge.

You begin to climb up...but at that moment, the drawbridge starts to open. It shoots downwards, sending you crashing to the ground.

SPLAT!

"Nice try. Not," says Maid Mousie.

A troop of guards marches out of the castle. The drawbridge is raised again.

You pick yourself up and stagger, bruised and battered, to where Maid Mousie is waiting for you.

"I think we need to find another way into the castle," you say.

"What a brilliant idea," smirks Mousie. "I knew you'd get there in the end."

Go to 27.

10

"Hurry up!" you mouth at Small John. He obeys but the tax collector hears the chopping noise. He urges his horses on and before you can do anything, he speeds past you.

Annoyed, you jump down from the tree on to the track to watch the collector and the money disappearing into the distance.

CREEEEEAK!

You look up to see the chopped tree falling towards you...

SPLAT!

Ouch!
Go back to 1.

11

You aim at the ropes binding the outlaws and shoot...PLAYED FOR AND GOT!

Your arrow slices through the ropes. Cluck and the other outlaws break free. Maid Mousie leaps down from the gallery.

"We have no weapons," shouts Bill Scarlett.

To try and seize the guards' weapons,
go to 19.

To use the food on the tables, go to 37.

12

You head towards the soldiers.

"Who are you and where are you going?" they demand.

"I am an archer going to Snottingham for the competition to win the Golden Sparrow," you say.

The leader looks at you suspiciously. "We're looking for **ROBIN HAMSTER.** He's an archer. I notice that you're a hamster and you've got a bow."

He turns to the other soldiers. "I reckon we've found him. **GRAB THE HAMSTER!**"

To FIGHT the soldiers, go to 8.

To get out of there NOW, go to 45.

13

"I'm not **ROBIN HAMSTER,**" you cry. "He's a lot smaller than me! And less cute."

But your protests are no use. The other outlaws watch on helplessly as you are taken away.

It looks like you're going to be caged up! Go back to 1.

14

You unload the chests of gold from the wagon.

"Thank the sheriff for the money," you laugh, and send the tax collector on his way. He speeds off on the wagon, cursing you.

As you are counting the gold, you hear shouts and the thundering of feet. Coming down the track is a troop of the sheriff's soldiers. The tax collector must have told them of your whereabouts! They head towards you, weapons raised.

If you want to stand UP and FIGHT for what's right, go to 31.

If you want to run away, go to 45.

When no one is looking, you make your way to the pie, peel back the lid and jump inside...

TWEET! TWEET! TWEET!

You nearly wet yourself as you are pecked at by four and twenty blackbirds.

Eventually, they calm down and you feel the pie being lifted up and carried out of the kitchen.

After a few minutes of an uncomfortable journey, you hear a burst of applause as the pie is taken into the main hall.

If you want to leap out RIGHT NOW, go to 25.

To wait until the pie is cut open, go to 44.

16

You take out your knife and cut at the rope net.

As you cut through the final bond, realisation suddenly hits you! You are a long way up from the ground. The only way is DOWN!

WAAHHH! SPLAT!

It's ROBIN HAMSTER pancake day!
Go back to 1.

You take your place at the back of the queuing archers and watch the other competitors shoot (and miss) at the target.

Soon, it is your turn. You step up, take aim and shoot.

BULLSEYE!

You take two more shots and again hit the target right in the centre.

YOU'VE WON THE GOLDEN SPARROW!

The crowd cheers as you stand before the sheriff, Grizzlybum and Princess Joan.

"Well done!" says the sheriff. "But there's only one archer in the land who can shoot as well as that. And that is ROBIN HAMSTER! You've fallen into our trap! Grab the hamster, guards!"

To protest your innocence, go to 13.

Call on the outlaws for help, go to 42.

To fight the soldiers on your own, go to 8.

18

You take hold of a rope tied to the tree. As the collector passes underneath you, you leap off the branch...

...fly over the top of the wagon and...

SPLAT!

You hit a tree...

You're not into the swing of things. Go back to 1.

"Grab the guards' weapons!" you cry.

The outlaws obey, but there are too many enemies to deal with...

CRASH! BANG! WALLOP!

Within minutes you and the other outlaws have been overwhelmed.

The sheriff stands over you. "To think you could ever defeat me! Cage this hamster!"

Well, that was brave (BUT STUPID)! Go back to 1.

"I think that's a jolly good idea," you say.

You head off and soon you are outside the city of Snottingham. Soldiers guard the city gate, checking everyone who wishes to enter. You look around and see a wooden ladder lying on the ground near the walls.

"How will we get into the city?" asks Bill Scarlett.

To put on a disguise to try and get through the main gate, go to 47.

To use the ladder to climb over the city walls, go to 38.

21

You draw your bow and take aim.

CRASH!

The wooden chandelier above smashes down on top of you, squashing you into hamster pizza.

If you'd moved and shown mercy, you wouldn't have got splattered!
Go back to 1.

22

"Grub's up!" announces Bill Scarlett. "Tuck in, Cluck!"

You and the outlaws start to eat.

"What about me?" asks the tax collector. "Do I get any food?"

"Not a chance," says Maid Mousie. "The poor can't eat because you take their money. Now we've taken yours, so you can't eat."

Her cousin, Maid Inchina, laughs. "The only taste you'll get is a taste of your own medicine!"

"Enjoy it while you can," snarls the collector. "You'd better eat up quickly..."

You wonder what he means.

Go to 3.

23

"**RUN!**" you order. The other outlaws obey.

You charge through the streets of Snottingham pursued by the guards. People dive out of the way as arrows fly around you. You turn a corner and see some stables ahead.

To hide in the stables, go to 49.

To turn and fight the soldiers, go to 31.

You make your way down the secret paths and tracks of the forest towards Snottingham, singing a merry song.

"With a hey nonny no
And a nonny, nonny no
And a hey nonny, nonny...

...OH NO!"

You suddenly find yourself hanging upside down in a net and dangling high up in a tree. You've been trapped!

If you want to try and cut yourself free, go to 16.

If you want to blow your horn for help, go to 34.

25

You leap up and burst through the pastry lid.

"**SURPRISE, SUR-PIES!**" you cry.

Everyone looks on amazed as you begin to shoot your arrows at the **BADDIES** sitting at the top table. Grizzlybum turns to run away, but he is too slow — your arrow hits him in the backside.

"Now his bum has something to be grizzly about!" you laugh.

To continue to shoot at the BADDIES, go to 30.

To fire at the ropes holding the outlaws, go to 11.

26

You signal to Small John to chop down a tree next to the forest track. He begins chopping at the trunk, but the wagon is getting nearer.

You're not sure Small John will get the job done in time.

If you want to tell him to chop faster, go to 10.

If you wish to swing on a rope and land on the wagon, go to 18.

If you wish to leap down and tell the collector to stop, go to 43.

27

"We need to find a secret passage to get into the castle," you say.

"You mean like this one?" says Mousie, pointing at a sign.

"Exactly!" you smile. "Well spotted."

You and Mousie make your way through the passage. It brings you out into a gallery overlooking the main hall, where a great feast is being held. The sheriff, Princess Joan and Grizzlybum are sitting at the top main table.

You see Cluck, Scarlett, Maid Inchina and Small John chained to a wall, being taunted by all the **BADDIES***!*

To leap down and rescue them, go to 32.
To think of a cunning plan to rescue them, go to 46.

The main square is full of people watching the archery competition. Looking down from a balcony is the sheriff and his chief baddie, Guy of Grizzlybum. They are joined by Princess Joan who looks very bored.

Archers are taking it in turn to shoot at a target set on a wooden stage.

If you want to enter the competition IMMEDIATELY, go to 4.

To watch some of the other competitors, go to 17.

"I will take part and win the sparrow!" you say.

"But Robin, it could be a trap," warns Maid Mousie. "Why else would the sheriff hold such a competition?"

"Good thinking," you say. "I don't want to put any of you at risk. I'll travel to Snottingham on my own."

The other outlaws protest but you have made up your mind.

"If I need you, I will blow my horn," you tell them. "But don't wait up!"

To head for Snottingham on the Great North Road, go to 41.

To go travel along the secret forest tracks, go to 24.

30

You aim at the sheriff, but the flying blackbirds get in your way and you have no clear shot. The **BADDIES** bravely dive under the table out of the way and the guards rush towards you.

To fight the guards, go to 8.

To shoot at the ropes holding the other outlaws, go to 11.

You draw your bow and shoot an arrow. The other outlaws follow your example but there are too many soldiers to deal with. They get closer and closer...

If you want to stand your ground, go to 8.
If you want to run away, faster than a hamster on a wheel, go to 45.

32

"Here's Robin!" you cry and grab hold of a tapestry to slide down it.

Unfortunately, the tapestry winds itself around you. You fall to the ground, trapped by the cloth. **"GET GEE OUT OG 'ERE..."** you mumble.

Then it all goes black as you feel a blow to your head.

That wasn't the rescue you planned! Go back to 1.

33

"Shut up, dog breath, and let me through," you tell the wolf.

BAD DECISION!

The wolf brings a large fist down on top of your head. **SMACK!**

Soldiers rush in to see what the commotion is all about. Before the outlaws can help you, the soldiers pull off your disguise.

The sheriff sees you. "It's ROBIN HAMSTER — arrest him!" he cries.

To try and run away, go to 45.
To protest your innocence, go to 13.

34

You blow your horn. Sometime later the outlaws appear.

"Are you hanging around for us?" laughs Friar Cluck.

"Cut the funnies and cut me down," you order.

Maid Mousie, who was starting to lower you down, suddenly cuts the rope holding you up.

You plummet downwards.

ARGGHHH! OUCH!

You lie battered and bruised on the floor.

"You did tell me to cut you down," says Maid Mousie. "Now, shall we all go to Snottingham?"

If you want to say yes, go to 20.
If you want to say no, go to 7.

35

You and Maid Mousie emerge from the dung pile and follow the guards from a distance.

You see your fellow outlaws being taken through the drawbridge and into the main castle of Snottingham. The drawbridge is raised behind them.

"How are we going to get in?" asks Maid Mousie.

To climb up the drawbridge, go to 9.
To try and find another way in, go to 27.

36

As the wagon hurtles towards you, you leap up and somersault on to it. You draw your bow, pressing the arrow into the collector's nose. "Stop the wagon **NOW**!" you order.

"I was always going to," says the tax collector. "Honestly..."

The wagon comes to a screeching halt as the other outlaws rush out from their hiding places and surround it.

To take the money and let the collector leave, go to 14.

To take the tax collector back to your camp, go to 48.

"**Food fight**!" you shout.

The outlaws obey and grab at the grub.

Soon, the hall is filled with flying pies, hunks of meat and bowls of cream. The sheriff's guards are taken out by mince pies, custard, hot potatoes and jellies.

The guards slip and slide on the food. Unable to fight, they quickly surrender. You tie up Grizzlybum and Princess Joan with a string of sausages and look around for the sheriff.

You see him near the entrance, trying to sneak away.

To shoot the sheriff, go to 21.
To take him prisoner, go to 6.

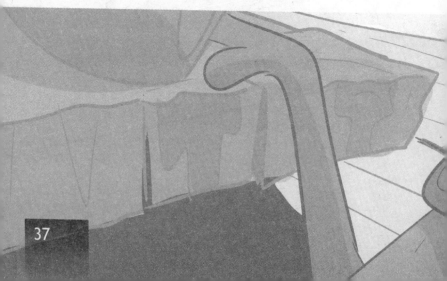

You take the ladder and, out of sight of the guards, place it against the city walls.

"You all go first and I'll bring up the rear," you tell the others.

Cluck leads the way, followed by the others. When they are all climbing the ladder, you follow them.

CRACK!

The ladder starts to **BREAK** under their weight. The outlaws shoot downwards.

THUD!

THUD!

THUD!

THUD!

They hit you, one after another. You weren't expecting to bring up the outlaws' rears like this! You decide to take the disguise option...

Go to 47.

You offer the tax collector some food.

He is puzzled at your generosity. "Why are you giving me food?"

Maid Mousie smiles. "Well, you have no money anymore, so you qualify as being POOR!"

Her cousin Maid Inchina laughs and hands over a plate of food.

As the tax collector eats, he tells you of an archery contest that is to take place in Snottingham.

"The greatest archers from across the country are competing," he says.

"What does the winner receive?" you ask.

"A golden sparrow," he says.

"Don't you mean a golden arrow?" asks Friar Cluck.

"No, it's a small prize," he replies. "But the true prize is being named the country's best archer."

Small John points at you. "That's you, Robin! We should go!"

Hmmm, you think. It could be a trap...

If you want to take part in the contest, go to 29.

To stay in the greenwood, go to 3.

You sneak over to the uncooked pie, climb under the pastry lid and wait.

Soon, you feel the pie being lifted up, before being placed back down.

A couple of minutes later you feel very hot and bothered. You smell something being cooked.

ARGHHHH!!!!

It's you! You leap out of the pie, but sadly for you, it's out of the frying pan and into the fire!

Your goose is cooked. Or rather, you are! Go back to 1.

You head towards Snottingham. The Great North Road is busy with traders going to market.

Ahead you see a troop of soldiers. They are stopping people and questioning them.

If you want to take your chance with the soldiers, go to 12.

If you want to travel along the secret tracks, go to 24.

"HELP ME!" you shout.

The outlaws spring to your defence and battle their way towards you. You all fight bravely, but there are too many guards to overcome...

To carry on fighting, go to 31.

To get out of there NOW, go to 23.

You leap from the tree, landing in front of the wagon.

You raise your bow and point your arrow at the tax collector. "Hand over the cash," you say.

"Not on your nelly, you hopeless hamster!" he replies and whips his horses into a gallop.

To order the other outlaws to attack, go to 5.

To leap on to the wagon, go to 36.

You stay crouching in the pie waiting for the lid to be cut open.

OW!

A knife plunges into the pie and into your bottom!

You leap out of the pie in **PAIN**! The sheriff, Princess Joan and Guy Grizzlybum look on amazed.

"Robin!" cries Friar Cluck.

"Get him!" screams the sheriff.

To shoot at the BADDIES, go to 30.

To fire at the ropes holding the outlaws, go to 11.

45

You turn to run but as you do so, you feel a pain in your backside!

OWWWW!

You've taken a shot to the bot!

Another arrow hits the spot and another and another. You hop around in pain before the soldiers grab you.

"The sheriff doesn't like you," they growl. "Have we made the point?"

They certainly have! And most of the points are in your bot!

Go back to 1.

You watch the servants serving the food.

"I've got an idea," you whisper to Maid Mousie. "You stay here and get ready for my signal. I'm going to head down to the kitchens."

You make your way down into the depths of the castle and find the kitchens. The busy cooks and servants don't give you a second look.

"Are those blackbird pies ready yet?" you hear the cook ask.

"One is cooked, one isn't," replies another cook.

You see two **ENORMOUS** pastry pies on the table.

To hide in the uncooked pie, go to 40.
To hide in the cooked pie, go to 15.

Using the tax collector's money, you pay some of the traders heading into the city for their clothes and a wagon.

The other outlaws hide under sacks and hay in the wagon.

You drive up to the gates. The guards look at you suspiciously.

"We're looking for a hamster," says one.

"I'm not a hamster, I'm a guinea pig," you reply.

"You're very small for a guinea pig."

"I've been ill."

The guard stares at you. "Alright, carry on."

You're in! You head for the main square where the competition is taking place.

Go to 28.

"We'll take the wagon back to the camp," you tell the others.

"What about me?" asks the tax collector.

"You're coming, too," you say. "We don't want you telling the sheriff where we are."

You make your way back to your camp and while you and the other outlaws count the **gold**, Small John and Bill Scarlett light a fire and cook up a feast.

If you want to let the tax collector share in your food, go to 39.

If you don't want to, go to 22.

You and Maid Mousie dive into the stables and into a huge pile of **horse dung**!

POOH!

The smell is **DISGUSTING!**

"That was a narrow escape," you whisper.

Maid Mousie looks puzzled.

"An *arrow* escape. Geddit?"

"Not funny," replies Maid Mousie.

The other outlaws are not as quick as you and Maid Mousie. You watch from your smelly hiding place as they are grabbed by the guards and led away...

If you want to try and rescue them, go to 35.

If you want to get out of Snottingham, go to 2.

Later that night, you are all back in the Greenwood, feasting and singing songs. The Golden Sparrow is in your possession, as is quite a lot of the **BADDIES'** gold...

Friar Cluck calls for silence. "Wherever there is injustice in this world there will be tales told about **ROBIN HAMSTER** and his Merry Menagerie, fighting against **BADDIES** everywhere!"

The outlaws cheer. You are a true hero!

I HERO
TOONS
INVASION OF THE BOTTY SNATCHERS
Steve Barlow · Steve Skidmore
Illustrated by Lee Robinson
EDGE

You are the only child of Professor Otto Lunch, the world's leading authority on *ALIEN LIFE FORMS*.

You are used to helping your father and his assistant Marcus in their experiments, and in their attempts to contact aliens via his Cosmic Broadcast (CB) Radio.

You and your father have been *BEAMING* messages to the stars for years, and never had a reply. But, one day, as you are sitting in your dad's lab reading your favourite sci-fi mag, the Cosmic Broadcast machine signals an incoming message

Go to 1.

Continue the adventure in:

About the 2Steves

"The 2Steves" are
Britain's most popular
writing double act
for young people,
specialising in comedy
and adventure. They

perform regularly in schools and libraries,
and at festivals, taking the power of words
and story to audiences of all ages.

Together they have written many books,
including the *I HERO Immortals* and *iHorror* series.

About the illustrator: Lee Robinson

Lee studied animation at Newcastle College and
went on to work on comics such as *Kung Fu
Panda* as well as running comicbook workshops
throughtout the northeast of England. When he's not
drawing, Lee loves running, reading and videogames.
He now lives in Edmonton, Canada, where's he's got
plenty of time to come up with crazy ideas while
waiting for the weather to warm up.

I HERO Legends — collect them all!

ATHENA
978 1 4451 5234 9 pb
978 1 4451 5235 6 ebook

BEOWULF
978 1 4451 5225 7 pb
978 1 4451 5226 4 ebook

KING ARTHUR
978 1 4451 5231 8 pb
978 1 4451 5232 5 ebook

FREYA
978 1 4451 5237 0 pb
978 1 4451 5238 7 ebook

HERCULES
978 1 4451 5228 8 pb
978 1 4451 5229 5 ebook

ROBIN HOOD
978 1 4451 5183 0 pb
978 1 4451 5184 7 ebook

Have you read the I HERO Monster Hunter series?

ALIEN
978 1 4451 5878 5 pb
978 1 4451 5876 1 ebook

GHOST
978 1 4451 5939 3 pb
978 1 4451 5940 9 ebook

MUTANT
978 1 4451 5945 4 pb
978 1445I 5946 1 ebook

VAMPIRE
978 1 4451 5936 2 pb
978 1 4451 5937 9 ebook

WEREWOLF
978 1 4451 5942 3 pb
978 1 4451 5943 0 ebook

ZOMBIE
978 1 4451 5935 5 pb
978 1 4451 5933 1 ebook

Also by the 2Steves...

978 1 4451 5104 5 pb
978 1 4451 5119 9 eBook

Ninja

Steve Barlow - Steve Skidmore

You are a skilled, stealthy ninja.
Your village has been attacked by a
warlord called Raiden. Now YOU must
go to his castle and stop him before
he destroys more lives.

978 1 4451 5101 4 pb
978 1 4451 5117 5 eBook

Warrior Princess

Steve Barlow - Steve Skidmore

You are the Warrior Princess.
Someone wants to steal the magical
ice diamonds from the Crystal
Caverns. YOU must discover who
it is and save your kingdom.

978 1 4451 5103 8 pb
978 1 4451 5121 2 eBook

Unicorn

Steve Barlow - Steve Skidmore

You are a magical unicorn.
Empress Yin Yang has stolen Carmine,
the red unicorn. Yin Yang wants to
destroy the colourful Rainbow Land.
YOU must stop her!

978 1 4451 5102 1 pb
978 1 4451 5124 3 eBook

Spy

Steve Barlow - Steve Skidmore

You are a spy, codenamed Scorpio.
Someone has taken control of secret
satellite laser weapons. YOU must find
out who is responsible and
stop their dastardly plans.